Traveler's Passport

United States and Canada

How To Use Your Traveler's Passport

The *Passport to the U.S.A. and Canada* has been designed to help travelers keep track of states and provinces visited on road trips. Each state entry is composed of a flag, a welcome sign, and a capital. Each province entry is composed of a provincial flag, a welcome sign, and a government building (Parliament building, Legislature building, Confederation building or Province House).

Enter the date for each visit on the color-coded block. The five U.S. regions are: the **West (green)**, **Midwest (red)**, **Southwest (purple)**, **Southeast (orange)**, and **Northeast (blue)**. The U.S. territories are represented by a modified purple rectangle. A red rectangle represents Canadian provinces and territories.

Colored outline maps of the U.S.A. and Canada will help in locating states and provinces. Travelers may keep a record of their visits by using a highlighter pen to color in locations visited. A trivia section is located in the back of the book along with license plates of the U.S.A. and Canada. Travelers can select the boxes next to the licenses that they have seen on their road trip(s).

A page is dedicated to brief expressions in Spanish for the Southwest U.S.A. and in French for Quebec and New Brunswick, Canada. A final section is provided for notes, contacts, and additional stamps available from national parks and monument visitor centers. Most U.S.A. state capital buildings have a state stamp located at their information desks.

My Passport Information

_____

Name

_____

Address

_____

City

_____

State / Province

_____

Postal Code

_____

Country

_____

E-mail

_____

Number of U.S. states and territories visited

_____

Number of Canadian provinces and territories visited

_____

Date of Road Trip(s)

United States of America

"Land of the Free"

Capital District: Washington, D.C.

Population: 311,591,917

Area: 3,794,083 sq. mi. (9,826,630 sq. km)

Language: English, Spanish

National Bird: Bald Eagle

National Flower: Rose

National Tree: Oak

States: 50

Territories: 5 (American Samoa, Guam, Northern Mariana Islands, Puerto Rico, & U.S. Virgin Islands)

"The Heart of Dixie"

Alabama

Capital:	Montgomery
Population:	4,802,740
Area (sq. mi.):	50,750
State Bird:	Yellowhammer
State Flower:	Camellia
State Tree:	Southern Pine
Economy:	Cattle, cotton, peanuts, dairy, watermelon

Date Visited:

Alabama workers built the first moon rocket.

"The Last Frontier"

Alaska

Capital:	Juneau
Population:	722,718
Area (sq. mi.):	570,374
State Bird:	Willow Ptarmigan
State Flower:	Forget-me-not
State Tree:	Sitka Spruce
Economy:	Dairy, cattle, hogs, barley, fish, crab, lumber

Date Visited:

Alaska was purchased from Russia in 1867 for $7,200,000, or two cents per acre.

Arizona
"The Grand Canyon State"

Date Visited:

Capital:	Phoenix
Population:	6,482,505
Area (sq. mi.):	113,642
State Bird:	Cactus Wren
State Flower:	Saguaro Cactus
State Tree:	Paloverde
Economy:	Cattle, lemons, pecans, watermelons, onions, lettuce

Arizona is the leading producer of copper in the U.S.A.

Arkansas
"The Natural State"

Date Visited:

Capital:	Little Rock
Population:	2,937,979
Area (sq. mi.):	52,075
State Bird:	Mockingbird
State Flower:	Apple Blossom
State Tree:	Pine Tree
Economy:	Rice, cattle, soybeans, cotton, eggs, turkeys, pecans

Sam Walton opened the first Wal-Mart store in Rogers.

"The Golden State"

California

Capital:	Sacramento
Population:	37,691,919
Area (sq. mi.):	155,973
State Bird:	California Quail
State Flower:	Golden Poppy
State Tree:	California Redwood
Economy:	Grapes, strawberries, almonds, oranges, cattle, dairy, dates

Date Visited:

One out of every eight U.S. residents lives in California.

"The Centennial State"

Colorado

Capital:	Denver
Population:	5,116,796
Area (sq. mi.):	103,729
State Bird:	Lark Bunting
State Flower:	R.M. Columbine
State Tree:	Blue Spruce
Economy:	Cattle, dairy, wheat, potatoes, eggs, sugar beets

Date Visited:

The world's first rodeo was held in Deer Trail on July 4th, 1869.

  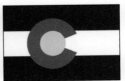

Connecticut

"The Constitution State"

Date Visited:

Capital: Hartford
Population: 3,580,709
Area (sq. mi.): 4,845
State Bird: Robin
State Flower: Mountain Laurel
State Tree: White Oak
Economy: Dairy, aguaculture, corn, cattle, maple products

Connecticut was the first state to issue car license plates in 1937.

Delaware

"The First State"

Date Visited:

Capital: Dover
Population: 907,135
Area (sq. mi.): 1,955
State Bird: Blue Hen Chicken
State Flower: Peach Blossom
State Tree: American Holly
Economy: Poultry, soybeans, potatoes, peas, cucumbers

Delaware was the first state to ratify the United States Constitution.

"The Sunshine State"

Florida

Capital: Tallahassee
Population: 19,057,542
Area (sq. mi.): 53,997
State Bird: Mockingbird
State Flower: Orange Blossom
State Tree: Cabbage Palmetto
Economy: Oranges, sugar cane, cattle, dairy, peanuts, nursery

Date Visited:

St. Augustine is the oldest continuously-occupied European settlement in the U.S.A.

"The Peach State"

Georgia

Capital: Atlanta
Population: 9,815,210
Area (sq. mi.): 57,919
State Bird: Brown Thrasher
State Flower: Cherokee Rose
State Tree: Live Oak
Economy: Poultry, cotton, eggs, peanuts, dairy, pecans, cattle

Date Visited:

Georgia is the leading producer of peanuts, peaches, and pecans in the U.S.A.

9

Hawaii

"The Aloha State"

Date Visited:

Capital: Honolulu
Population: 1,374,810
Area (sq. mi.): 6,423
State Bird: Nene
State Flower: Hibiscus
State Tree: Kukui
Economy: Pineapples, coffee, sugar cane, taro, cattle

Hawaii is the only state that produces both coffee and pineapples.

Idaho

"The Gem State"

Date Visited:

Capital: Boise
Population: 1,584,985
Area (sq. mi.): 82,751
State Bird: Mountain Bluebird
State Flower: Syringa
State Tree: Western White Pine
Economy: Dairy, cattle, potatoes, wheat, hay, sugar beats, apples

Idaho is the largest producer of potatoes in the U.S.A.

"The Prairie State"

Illinois

Capital: Springfield
Population: 12,869,257
Area (sq. mi.): 55,593
State Bird: Cardinal
State Flower: Native Violet
State Tree: White Oak
Economy: Soybeans, hogs, eggs, corn, dairy, turkeys, cabbage

The world's first skyscraper was built in Chicago in 1885.

"The Hoosier State"

Indiana

Capital: Indianapolis
Population: 6,516,922
Area (sq. mi.): 35,870
State Bird: Cardinal
State Flower: Peony
State Tree: Yellow Poplar
Economy: Soybeans, hogs, hay, corn, tobacco, watermelon

The Raggedy Ann doll was made in Indianapolis by Marcella Gruelle in 1914.

Iowa

"The Hawkeye State"

Date Visited:

Capital: Des Moines
Population: 3,062,309
Area (sq. mi.): 55,875
State Bird: Eastern Goldfinch
State Flower: Wild Rose
State Tree: Oak
Economy: Corn, hogs, honey, dairy, wheat, oats, apples

The world's largest cereal company, Quaker Oats, is located in Cedar Rapids.

Kansas

"The Sunflower State"

Date Visited:

Capital: Topeka
Population: 2,871,238
Area (sq. mi.): 55,875
State Bird: Western Meadowlark
State Flower: Sunflower
State Tree: Cottonwood
Economy: Wheat, cattle, soybeans, hogs, dairy, sorghum, pecans

The Pizza Hut restaurant chain was founded in Wichita.

"The Bluegrass State"

Kentucky

Capital:	Frankfort
Population:	4,369,356
Area (sq. mi.):	39,732
State Bird:	Cardinal
State Flower:	Goldenrod
State Tree:	Yellow Poplar
Economy:	Horses, poultry, hogs, apples, dairy, hay, cattle

Date Visited:

The first Kentucky Fried Chicken restaurant was established in Corbin.

"The Pelican State"

Louisiana

Capital:	Baton Rouge
Population:	4,574,836
Area (sq. mi.):	43,566
State Bird:	Brown Pelican
State Flower:	Magnolia
State Tree:	Bald Cypress
Economy:	Sugar cane, rice, cattle, soybeans, sweet potatoes

Date Visited:

Louisiana's state capitol building is the tallest in the U.S.A.

Maine
"The Pine Tree State"

Date Visited:

Capital: Augusta
Population: 1,328,188
Area (sq. mi.): 30,865
State Bird: Chickadee
State Flower: White Pine Cone and Tassel
State Tree: Eastern White Pine
Economy: Dairy, potatoes, corn, aquaculture, cattle, maple products

Nearly 90 percent of the lobster supply of the U.S.A. is caught off the coast of Maine.

Maryland
"The Old Line State"

Date Visited:

Capital: Annapolis
Population: 5,828,289
Area (sq. mi.): 9,775
State Bird: Baltimore Oriole
State Flower: Black-eyed Susan
State Tree: White Oak
Economy: Poultry, cattle, eggs, watermelon, tobacco, soybeans

Baseball player Babe Ruth was born in Maryland.

"The Bay State"

Massachusetts

Capital: Boston
Population: 9,876,187
Area (sq. mi.): 7,838
State Bird: Chickadee
State Flower: Mayflower
State Tree: American Elm
Economy: Cranberries, dairy, apples, tobacco, maple products, cattle

Date Visited:

America's first subway system was built in Boston in 1897.

"The Great Lakes State"

Michigan

Capital: Lansing
Population: 9,876,187
Area (sq. mi.): 56,809
State Bird: Robin
State Flower: Apple Blossom
State Tree: White Pine
Economy: Dairy, soybeans, hogs, grapes, apples, cherries, asparagus

Date Visited:

Michigan is the leading state in boat registrations in the U.S.A.

Minnesota

"The Gopher State"

Date Visited:

Capital:	St. Paul
Population:	5,344,861
Area (sq. mi.):	79,617
State Bird:	Common Loon
State Flower:	Pink & White Lady Slipper
State Tree:	Norway Pine
Economy:	Corn, hogs, soybeans, dairy, cattle, turkeys, sugar beets

The famous Mayo Clinic medical center is located in Rochester.

Mississippi

"The Magnolia State"

Date Visited:

Capital:	Jackson
Population:	2,978,512
Area (sq. mi.):	49,914
State Bird:	Mockingbird
State Flower:	Southern Magnolia
State Tree:	Magnolia
Economy:	Poultry, cotton, rice, cattle, sweet potatoes, pecans

The famous singer Elvis Presley was born in Tupelo on January 8, 1935.

"The Show Me State"

Missouri

Capital: Jefferson City
Population: 6,010,688
Area (sq. mi.): 68,898
State Bird: Bluebird
State Flower: Hawthorn
State Tree: Flowering Dogwood
Economy: Soybeans, cattle, corn, rice, grapes, honey, turkeys, cotton

Date Visited:

Kansas City has more boulevards than any other city in the world, except Paris.

"The Treasure State"

Montana

Capital: Helena
Population: 998,199
Area (sq. mi.): 145,556
State Bird: Western Meadowlark
State Flower: Bitterroot
State Tree: Ponderosa Pine
Economy: Cattle, wheat, barley, sugar beets, sheep, oats, wool

Date Visited:

Yellowstone National Park is widely held to be first national park in the world.

Nebraska
"The Cornhusker State"

Date Visited:

Capital: Lincoln
Population: 1,842,641
Area (sq. mi.): 76,878
State Bird: Western Meadowlark
State Flower: Goldenrod
State Tree: Cottonwood
Economy: Cattle, corn, soybeans, wheat, dairy, eggs, potatoes

The Reuben sandwich originated in Nebraska.

Nevada
"The Silver State"

Date Visited:

Capital: Carson City
Population: 2,723,322
Area (sq. mi.): 109,806
State Bird: Mountain Bluebird
State Flower: Sagebrush
State Tree: Bristlecone Pine
Economy: Cattle, hay, dairy, wheat, garlic, honey, hogs, barley

Nevada is the leading state in U.S. gold mining.

"The Granite State"

New Hampshire

Capital: Concord
Population: 1,318,194
Area (sq. mi.): 8,969
State Bird: Purple Finch
State Flower: Purple Lilac
State Tree: White Birch
Economy: Dairy, apples, cattle, corn, eggs, maple products

New Hampshire established the first free public library in Peterborough in 1833.

"The Garden State"

New Jersey

Capital: Trenton
Population: 8,821,155
Area (sq. mi.): 7,419
State Bird: Eastern Goldfinch
State Flower: Purple Violet
State Tree: Red Oak
Economy: Horses, blueberries, dairy, cranberries asparagus

New Jersey is the most densely populated state in the U.S.A.

New Mexico   "The Land of Enchantment"

Date Visited:

Capital: Santa Fe
Population: 2,082,224
Area (sq. mi.): 121,365
State Bird: Roadrunner
State Flower: Yucca
State Tree: Piñon Pine
Economy: Dairy, pecans, cotton, chile peppers, peanuts, onions

Santa Fe is the highest state capital in the U.S.A. at 7,000 feet.

New York   "The Empire State"

Date Visited:

Capital: Albany
Population: 19,465,197
Area (sq. mi.): 47,224
State Bird: Bluebird
State Flower: Rose
State Tree: Sugar Maple
Economy: Dairy apples, hay, peas, potatoes, ducks, onions, grapes

Arthur Eldred of Troop 1 in Oceanside received the first Eagle Scout award in 1912.

"The Tar Heel State"

North Carolina

Capital: Raleigh
Population: 9,656,401
Area (sq. mi.): 48,718
State Bird: Cardinal
State Flower: Flowering Dogwood
State Tree: Pine
Economy: Poultry, hogs, eggs, dairy, turkeys, cotton, wheat, tobacco

Date Visited:

Winston-Salem is the home of the Krispy Kreme doughnut.

"The Peace Garden State"

North Dakota

Capital: Bismarck
Population: 683,932
Area (sq. mi.): 68,994
State Bird: Western Meadowlark
State Flower: Wild Prairie Rose
State Tree: American Elm
Economy: Wheat, cattle, sugar beets, soybeans, dry beans, sunflowers

Date Visited:

North Dakota is the leading producer of sunflowers in the U.S.A.

Ohio

"The Buckeye State"

Date Visited:

Capital:	Columbus
Population:	11,544,951
Area (sq. mi.):	40,953
State Bird:	Cardinal
State Flower:	Scarlet Carnation
State Tree:	Buckeye
Economy:	Soy beans, corn, hay, poultry, turkeys, tomatoes

Akron is the rubber capital of the world.

Oklahoma

"The Sooner State"

Date Visited:

Capital:	Oklahoma City
Population:	3,791,508
Area (sq. mi.):	68,679
State Bird:	Scissor-tailed-flycatcher
State Flower:	Mistletoe
State Tree:	Eastern Redbud
Economy:	Cattle, hogs, poultry, wheat, dairy, pecans, rye, watermelon

Famous American humorist and cowboy Will Rogers was born in Oklahoma.

"The Beaver State"

Oregon

Capital: Salem
Population: 3,871,859
Area (sq. mi.): 96,003
State Bird: Western Meadowlark
State Flower: Oregon Grape
State Tree: Douglas Fir
Economy: Cattle, dairy, hay, hops, onions, potatoes, hazel nuts, cherries

Date Visited:

Crater Lake is the deepest lake in the U.S.A.

"The Keystone State"

Pennsylvania

Capital: Harrisburg
Population: 12,742,886
Area (sq. mi.): 44,820
State Bird: Ruffed Grouse
State Flower: Mountain Laurel
State Tree: Hemlock
Economy: Dairy, cattle, eggs, hogs, mushrooms, poultry, potatoes

Date Visited:

Hershey is considered the chocolate capital of the U.S.A.

Rhode Island

"The Ocean State"

Date Visited:

Capital:	Providence
Population:	1,051,302
Area (sq. mi.):	1,045
State Bird:	Rhode Island Red
State Flower:	Violet
State Tree:	Red Maple
Economy:	Corn, dairy, potatoes, corn, apples, hay, honey

The International Tennis Hall of Fame is located in Newport.

South Carolina

"The Palmetto State"

Date Visited:

Capital:	Columbia
Population:	4,679,230
Area (sq. mi.):	30,111
State Bird:	Carolina Wren
State Flower:	Carolina Jessamine
State Tree:	Palmetto
Economy:	Turkeys, dairy, cattle, pecans, peanuts, watermelons

The first battle of the American Civil War took place at Fort Sumter.

"The Mount Rushmore State"

South Dakota

Capital: Pierre
Population: 824,082
Area (sq. mi.): 30,111
State Bird: Pheasant
State Flower: Pasque Flower
State Tree: White Spruce
Economy: Cattle, corn, hogs, rye wheat, soy beans, honey

The world's largest petrified wood park is located in Lemmon.

"The Volunteer State"

Tennessee

Capital: Nashville
Population: 6,403,353
Area (sq. mi.): 41,220
State Bird: Mockingbird
State Flower: Iris
State Tree: Tulip Poplar
Economy: Cattle, poultry, wool, squash, peaches, hay, aquaculture

The famous frontiersman Davy Crockett was born in Greene County.

Texas

"The Lone Star State"

Date Visited:

Capital:	Austin
Population:	25,674,681
Area (sq. mi.):	264,914
State Bird:	Mockingbird
State Flower:	Bluebonnet
State Tree:	Pecan
Economy:	Cattle, cotton, hay, rice, poultry, wheat, peanuts, pecans

The Alamo is located in San Antonio.

Utah

"The Beehive State"

Date Visited:

Capital:	Salt Lake City
Population:	2,817,222
Area (sq. mi.):	82,168
State Bird:	Seagull
State Flower:	Sego Lily
State Tree:	Blue Spruce
Economy:	Cattle, dairy, apples, cherries, peaches, pears, oats, apricots

Utah comes from the Native American Ute Tribe and means "People of the Mountains."

"The Green Mountain State"

Vermont

Capital: Montpelier
Population: 626,431
Area (sq. mi.): 9,249
State Bird: Hermit Thrush
State Flower: Red Clover
State Tree: Sugar Maple
Economy: Dairy, cattle, apples, maple products, eggs, honey

Date Visited:

Montpelier is the smallest state capital in the U.S.A.

"Old Dominion"

Virginia

Capital: Richmond
Population: 8,096,604
Area (sq. mi.): 39,598
State Bird: Cardinal
State Flower: Dogwood
State Tree: Flowering Dogwood
Economy: Poultry, cattle, dairy, turkeys, tobacco, peanuts, corn

Date Visited:

Virginia is the home base for the U.S. Navy's Atlantic Fleet.

Washington

"The Evergreen State"

Date Visited:

Capital:	Olympia
Population:	6,830,038
Area (sq. mi.):	66,581
State Bird:	Willow Goldfinch
State Flower:	Rhododendron
State Tree:	Western Hemlock
Economy:	Apples, cherries, hops, potatoes, wheat, cattle, mint

Washington is the leading producer of apples in the world.

West Virginia

"The Mountain State"

Date Visited:

Capital:	Charleston
Population:	1,855,364
Area (sq. mi.):	24,087
State Bird:	Cardinal
State Flower:	Rhododendron
State Tree:	Sugar Maple
Economy:	Poultry, cattle, tobacco, aquaculture, honey, apples, corn

West Virginia was a part of Virginia until Virginia seceded from the Union in 1861.

"The Badger State"

Wisconsin

Capital: Madison
Population: 5,711,767
Area (sq. mi.): 54,314
State Bird: Robin
State Flower: Wood Violet
State Tree: Sugar Maple
Economy: Dairy, cattle, hogs, cranberries, apples, peas, honey

Date Visited:

Wisconsin is the dairy capital of the U.S.A.

"The Equality State"

Wyoming

Capital: Cheyenne
Population: 568,158
Area (sq. mi.): 97,105
State Bird: Meadowlark
State Flower: Indian Paintbrush
State Tree: Cottonwood
Economy: Cattle, hay, honey, sugar beets, sheep, beans, barley

Date Visited:

Wyoming was the first state to grant women the right to vote in the U.S.A.

The United States Territories

American Samoa

Guam

Northern Mariana Islands

Puerto Rico

U.S. Virgin Islands

District of Columbia

"Let God be First"

American Samoa

Capital: Pago Pago
Population: 54,719
Area (sq. mi.): 76
Economy: Coconuts, cacao, fruits, vegetables, fish, lumber

Date Visited:

The Samoan alphabet has only fourteen letters: five vowels and nine consonants.

"Where America's Day Begins"

Guam

Capital: Agana
Population: 160,378
Area (sq. mi.): 209
Economy: Fruits & vegetables, shrimp, livestock, bananas

Date Visited:

Guam was first inhabited approximately 4,000 years ago by the Chamorro people.

Northern Mariana Islands   "Land of the Valiant Lord"

Date Visited:

Capital: Saipan
Population: 51,170
Area (sq. mi.): 185
Economy: Copra, livestock, fish, fruits & vegetables

Active volcanoes exist on several islands, including Anatahan, Pagan and Agrihan.

Puerto Rico   "All-Star Island"

Date Visited:

Capital: San Juan
Population: 3,690,923
Area (sq. mi.): 3,435
Economy: Chemicals, clothing, fruits & vegetables, fish, sugar

El Yunque is the only tropical rainforest in the U.S. National Forest System.

"American Paradise"

U. S. Virgin Islands

Capital: Charlotte Amalie
Population: 104,737
Area (sq. mi.): 133
Economy: Manufacturing, fruits & vegetables, rum

Date Visited:

The United States bought the U.S. Virgin Islands from Denmark in 1917.

Washington D.C.

District of Columbia

Capital: Washington, D.C.
Population: 646,449
Area (sq. mi.): 68.3
Economy: Federal Government, tourism, education, finance, public policy, scientific research

Date Visited:

D.C. is under the jurisdiction of the U.S. Congress and is not a part of any state.

Canada

"From Sea to Sea"

National Capital Region: Ottawa

Population: 35,158,300

Area: 9,984,670 sq. km (3,855,103 sq. mi.)

Language: English, French

National Animal: Beaver

National Sports: Hockey & Lacrosse

National Tree: Maple

Provinces: 10

Territories: 3 (Northwest Territories, Nunavut, Yukon)

"Wild Rose Country"

Alberta

Capital: Edmonton
Population: 3,645,257
Area (sq. km.): 640,082
Provincial Bird: Great Horned Owl
Provincial Flower: Wild Rose
Provincial Tree: Lodgepole Pine
Economy: Coal, oil, natural gas, oats, livestock, canola, barley, wheat

Date Visited:

Alberta was named after Princess Louise Caroline Alberta, daughter of Queen Victoria.

"Beautiful British Columbia"

British Columbia

Capital: Victoria
Population: 4,400,057
Area (sq. km.): 922,509
Provincial Bird: Steller's Jay
Provincial Flower: Pacific Dogwood
Provincial Tree: Western Red Cedar
Economy: Lumber, mining, fish, fruit & vegetables

Date Visited:

British Columbia has the largest Chinese community in Canada.

39

Manitoba

"Land of 100,000 Lakes"

Date Visited:

Capital: Winnipeg
Population: 1,208,268
Area (sq. km.): 552,330
Provincial Bird: Great Grey Owl
Provincial Flower: Prairie Crocus
Provincial Tree: White Spruce
Economy: Mining, fish, wheat, dairy, livestock

Manitoba is a world leader in the production of nickel.

New Brunswick

"The Loyalist Province"

Date Visited:

Capital: Fredericton
Population: 751,171
Area (sq. km.): 71,377
Provincial Bird: Blackcapped Chickadee
Provincial Flower: Purple Violet
Provincial Tree: Balsam Fir
Economy: Mining, fish, shell fish (lobster & Crab), fruit, dairy, forestry

New Brunswick is Canada's only official bilingual province (English & French).

"The Rock"   Newfoundland & Labrador

Capital: St. John's
Population: 514,536
Area (sq. km.): 370,511
Provincial Bird: Atlantic Puffin
Provincial Flower: Pitcher Plant
Provincial Tree: Black Spruce
Economy: Fish products, oil, gas, iron ore,
newsprint, electricity, shell fish

Date Visited:

Norse Vikings first visited the northern tip of Newfoundland around 1000 A.D.

"Canada's Atlantic Playground"   Nova Scotia

Capital: Halifax
Population: 921,727
Area (sq. km.): 52,939
Provincial Bird: Osprey
Provincial Flower: Mayflower
Provincial Tree: Red Spruce
Economy: Coal, fish, lobsters, lumber, pulp,
paper, gypsum, blueberries

Date Visited:

Nova Scotia means "New Scotland" in Latin.

Ontario

"The Heartland Province"

Date Visited:

Capital: Toronto
Population: 12,851,821
Area (sq. km.): 908,608
Provincial Bird: Common Loon
Provincial Flower: White Trillium
Provincial Tree: Eastern White Pine
Economy: Minerals, lumber, dairy, grain, manufacturing, fruits & vegetables

Toronto is Canada's financial center.

Prince Edward Island

"Birthplace of Confederation"

Date Visited:

Capital: Charlottetown
Population: 140,204
Area (sq. km.): 5,686
Provincial Bird: Blue Jay
Provincial Flower: Lady Slipper
Provincial Tree: Red Oak
Economy: Potatoes, fish, fruits & vegetables (apples, onions, blueberries)

Prince Edward Island's soil is rust-red from a high iron oxide content.

"The Beautiful Province"

Quebec

Capital:	Quebec City
Population:	7,903,001
Area (sq. km.):	1,356,547
Provincial Bird:	Snowy Owl
Provincial Flower:	Blue Flag (Iris)
Provincial Tree:	Yellow Birch
Economy:	Minerals, pulp, paper, lumber, maple syrup, dairy, fruits & vegetables

Date Visited:

French is Quebec's sole official language.

"Canada's Bread Basket"

Saskatchewan

Capital:	Regina
Population:	1,033,381
Area (sq. km.):	588,239
Provincial Bird:	Sharp-tailed Grouse
Provincial Flower:	Western Red Lilly
Provincial Tree:	White Birch
Economy:	Wheat, canola, oats, barley, flax, lentils, oil, natural gas, minerals

Date Visited:

First designated bird sanctuary in N. America was founded in Saskatchewan in 1887.

43

Northwest Territories

"North of Sixty"

Capital:	Yellow Knife
Population:	41,462
Area (sq. km.):	1,143,793
Provincial Bird:	Gyrfalcon
Provincial Flower:	Mountain Avens
Provincial Tree:	Tamarack Larch
Economy:	Oil, natural gas, fishing, diamonds, trapping (mink, wolf, lynx, fox)

The Mackenzie River is Canada's longest river (1738 km).

Nunavut

"Our Land"

Capital:	Iqaluit
Population:	31,906
Area (sq. km.):	1,877,788
Provincial Bird:	Rock Ptarmigan
Provincial Flower:	Purple Saxifrage
Economy:	Gold, diamonds, fish, Inuit arts & crafts, vegetables in green houses

Iqaluit is Canada's northernmost capital.

"Land of the Midnight Sun"

Yukon

Capital: Whitehorse
Population: 33,897
Area (sq. km.): 474,713
Provincial Bird: Common Raven
Provincial Flower: Fireweed
Provincial Tree: Subalpine Fir
Economy: Mining gold, zinc, lead, trapping beaver, lynx, weasel, fox, mink

Date Visited:

Yukon is larger than Belgium, Denmark, Germany, and the Netherlands combined.

Ottawa

National Capital Region

Capital: Ottawa
Population: 883,391
Area (sq. km.): 2,778
Economy: Public Services of Canada, high-tech industries, health services and education

Date Visited:

The motto of the City of Ottawa is "Advance-Ottawa-En Avant."

Trivia Questions   U.S.A. & Canada

1. List the five regions of the U.S.A.:

   _____, _____, _____, _____, _____.

2. Which is the largest state in area:

   _____, and the smallest: _____.

3. Which Canadian province is largest in area:

   _____, and the smallest: _____.

4. Number of U.S.A. states: _____,
   and Canadian provinces: _____.

5. Name the five U.S.A. territories:

   _____, _____, _____, _____, _____.

6. Name the three Canadian territories:

   _____, _____, _____.

7. Name the slogan of the U.S.A.:

   _____.

8. Name the slogan of Canada:

   _____.

9. Population of the U.S.A.: _____,
   and the population of Canada: _____.

10. National tree of the U.S.A.: _____.

11. National tree of Canada: _____.

12. Languages of Canada: _____, _____.

13. Languages of the U.S.A.: _____, _____.

Trivia answers on page 48

English, French, & Spanish   Top Ten Phrases

ENGLISH	FRENCH	PRONUNCIATION
Welcome	Bienvenue	bee-ehn-veh-new
Hello	Bonjour	bohn-zhoor
Please	S'il vous plaît	seel-voo-play
Thank you	Merci	mehr-see
You are welcome	De rien	duh-ryang
Good morning	Bonjour	bohn-zhoor
Good afternoon	Bonjour	bohn-zhoor
Good evening	Bonsoir	bohn-swahr
Good day	Bonjour	bohn-zhoor
Goodbye	au revoir	oh-ruh-vwahr

ENGLISH	SPANISH	PRONUNCIATION
Welcome	Bienvenido	be-en-vay-nee-do
Hello	Hola	o-la
Please	Por favor	por-fa-vor
Thank you	Gracias	gra-syas
You are welcome	De nada	de-na-da
Good morning	Buenos días	bwe-nos-dee-as
Good afternoon	Buenas tardes	bwe-nas-tar-des
Good evening	Buenas noches	bwe-nas-no-ches
Good day	Buenos días	bwe-nos-dee-as
Goodbye	Adiós	a-dyos

Trivia Answers U.S.A. & Canada

1. West, Midwest, Southwest, Southeast, Northeast
2. Alaska, Rhode Island
3. Quebec, Prince Edward Island
4. States: 50, Provinces: 10
5. American Samoa, Guam, Northern Marianas, Puerto Rico, U.S. Virgin Islands
6. Northwest Territories, Nunavut, Yukon
7. Land of the Free
8. From Sea to Sea
9. Population: US 311,591,917   Canada 35,158,300
10. Oak
11. Maple
12. English, French
13. English, Spanish

U.S.A. License Plate Search

JAN · Sweet Home · 10
47C72N2
Alabama

APR · ALASKA · 09
FGM774
CELEBRATING STATEHOOD 1959-2009

JUN · ARIZONA · 08
AAG1921
GRAND CANYON STATE

6 · Arkansas · 07
514 KZE
The Natural State

NOV · California · 2010
6JIV337

038 · NAV
COLORADO

Connecticut
285 · XHK
Constitution State

THE FIRST STATE
731260
DELAWARE 12

MYFLORIDA.COM · 06-10
981 XXH
SUNSHINE STATE

· GEORGIA · .gov
BVN 0669
CLAYTON APR

HAWAII · APR
HGX 212
ALOHA STATE

Scenic IDAHO
1A VB713
FAMOUS POTATOES

Illinois 01-08
G34 3404

02-28 29 · Hamilton 09
221TAN
INDIANA

Iowa
180 RCQ
LINN

JO · KANSAS · APR
604 ADU

Kentucky
547 KPE
FAYETTE

Louisiana
OIT 643
Sportsman's Paradise

· MAINE · MAY
7687 PG
Vacationland 08

8 · Maryland · 09
3DD B31
www.maryland.gov

MAR · Massachusetts · 11
432 EY3
The Spirit of America

MICHIGAN MAY
BXC 2341
www.Michigan.gov

EXPLORE Minnesota.com
845 CTC
JUL 10,000 lakes 10

MISSISSIPPI
TAD 856
TATE
01 09

APR · Missouri
FC6 B1R

TREASURE STATE
6 · 09241A
MONTANA - 10

Nebraska 10
5 - D2772

49

❏ NEVADA 617·VBR — THE SILVER STATE

❏ PENNSYLVANIA HFZ·5473 — visitPA.com

❏ West Virginia 6NM 162 — Wild, Wonderful

❏ LIVE FREE OR DIE 275 7814 — NEW HAMPSHIRE

❏ Rhode Island 934·219 — Ocean State

❏ WISCONSIN 271-LDZ — America's Dairyland

❏ New Jersey ZWT·69X — Garden State

❏ South Carolina CDI 441 — TRAVEL2SC.COM

❏ 22·13406 — WYOMING

❏ CENTENNIAL 1912-2012 LLY·441 — NEW MEXICO LAND OF ENCHANTMENT

❏ 29C A53 — GREAT FACES. GREAT PLACES.

U.S. Territories

❏ NEW YORK FAE·5954 — EMPIRE STATE

❏ MAY Tennessee 999–QLM — DAVIDSON

❏ CENTENNIAL 2000 7588 — AMERICAN SAMOA

❏ First in Flight WYF-8749 — NORTH CAROLINA

❏ TEXAS BC5·X489 — The Lone Star State

❏ GUAM U.S.A. 4817PDE — TANO Y CHAMORRO

❏ Discover the Spirit JAX 802 — NORTH DAKOTA PEACE GARDEN STATE

❏ UTAH Z80 8CJ — LIFE ELEVATED

❏ COMMONWEALTH 9802 — NORTHERN MARIANA IS

❏ Ohio FAR 2602

❏ Vermont DFC 620 — Green Mountain State

❏ PUERTO RICO GERRY — Isla Del Encanto

❏ OKLAHOMA 307BEE — NATIVE AMERICA

❏ VIRGINIA XXJ-6610

❏ U.S. VIRGIN ISLANDS C·42173 — AMERICAN PARADISE

❏ Oregon 230 BXE

❏ WASHINGTON ACG8095 — EVERGREEN STATE

Canadian License Plate Search

- [ ] Alberta — NOV — UJE · 444 — Wild Rose Country
- [ ] Beautiful British Columbia — MBG · 091 — JUL
- [ ] *friendly* Manitoba — ACC 678 — 14 — SHALOM
- [ ] New Brunswick — GGG-693
- [ ] Newfoundland & Labrador — COG 274 — APR 2011 — APR
- [ ] NOVA SCOTIA — AAA · 000 — CANADA'S OCEAN PLAYGROUND
- [ ] ONTARIO — ESM · 32 — YOURS TO DISCOVER
- [ ] Confederation Bridge — VS 111 — Prince Edward Island
- [ ] Québec — 756 JWB — Je me souviens

- [ ] Saskatchewan — HJB 546 — OCT '77

Canadian Territories

- [ ] SPECTACULARNWT — 000 — NORTHWEST TERRITORIES

- [ ] EXPLORE CANADA'S ARCTIC — 000 — NUNAVUT

- [ ] The Klondike — ASJ 43 — MAY — Yukon

Notes Pages

Use these pages for journal entries, or the phone numbers and addresses of people you meet during your travels.

Stamp Pages

You may use these pages for stamps from U.S. State Capitals, National Parks, or Monuments. Many sites have commemorative stamps located at an information desk or booth.

Travelers Passport U.S.A. & Canada　　Photo Credits

Welcome Signs U.S.A.
AK: Richard Martin;
OR: Oregon Department Transportation;
Other 48 States: Dr. Ron Snipe.

Welcome Signs Canada
Alberta: Raymond Hitchcock; British Columbia: Hans-Peter Eckhardt; Manitoba: Government of Manitoba; New Brunswick: Dr Ron Snipe; Newfoundland: Government of Newfoundland; NW Territories: Government Tourist Office; Nova Scotia: Dennis Jarvis; Nunavut: Government of Nunavut; Ontario: Dr. Ron Snipe; Prince Edward Island: Government of P.E.I.; Quebec: Dr. Ron Snipe; Saskatchewan: Tdot778; Yukon: ZOOP; National Capital Region: public domain.

U.S.A. Capitals
All 50 photos: Dr. Ron Snipe, 2005-2013.

U.S.A. Territories
American Samoa: (l) Thomas Marki, (r) miles530 of NOAA; Guam: (l) USAF-A.M. Lawrence, (r) Abasaa; Northern Marianas: Abasaa; Puerto Rico: Dr. Ron Snipe; U.S. Virgin Islands: (l) Johnpaulribaudo, (r) smallbones.

Canadian Government Buildings
Alberta: Zeitlupe; British Columbia: Dr. Ron Snipe; Manitoba: Canuks4ever83; New Brunswick: Benson Kua; Newfoundland: David P. Janes; Northwest Territories: wintercity296; Nova Scotia: Louperivois; Nunavut: Ansgar Walk; Ontario: Benson Kua; Prince Edward Island: Share Bear; Quebec: Christopher Finot; Saskatchewan: M Readey; Yukon: OwnWork.

U.S.A. License Plates
All photos public domain.

U.S.A. Territories License Plates
American Samoa: monroedictator; Guam, Northern Mariana Islands, Puerto Rico, U.S. Virgin Islands: Jerry Woody.

Canadian License Plates
Alberta, British Columbia, Manitoba, NW Territories, Saskatchewan: Jerry Woody; Ontario, Prince Edward Island: Dickelbers; New Brunswick: Campbell Showing; Newfoundland: Ramses31; Nova Scotia: Government of Nova Scotia; Nunavut: Government of Nunavut; Quebec: Lionel Bartel; Yukon: RobinsonCrusoe.

National Capital Buildings
U.S.A. Capitol Buildings: pg. 4-Martin Falbisoner; pg. 35-Architect of the Capitol. Canadian Parliament: pg. 38-Steven W. Dengler; pg. 45-Public Domain.

Maps, U.S.A. and Canada
U.S.A. Outline Map: Public Domain; Canada Outline Map: Brock University Map, Data & GIS Library

Author: Ron Snipe, Ph.D

Editor in Chief: Elizabeth Snipe

Consultant/Designer: Zachary Snipe, Esq.

Print Production:
Mike Burk Production Services
www.mikeburk.com